GET SET, SCORE!

Welcome to the world of football. This goal-tastic Annual 2022 has all you need to know about the great game, and is bursting with a whole score of puzzles and activities to keep you entertained during half time. Are you ready to play?

P8-9 SPOT THE TOP SCORERS IN THE GIANT GRID!

SKETCH A NEW KIT FOR YOUR TEAM, AS WELL AS SOME BLINGIN' BOOTS FOR YOU!

DISCOVER FUN FACTS ABOUT THE WORLD'S MOST AWESOME SOCCER CLUBS.

P48-49

COMPLETE SOME TRICKY CHALLENGES TO MAKE SURE YOUR FOOTY SKILLS ARE UP TO SCRATCH.

P72-73

TEST YOUR UEFA CHAMPIONS LEAGUE KNOWLEDGE WITH A QUICK-FIRE QUIZ.

COMPLETE PUZZLES, PLAY GAMES AND CREATE YOUR DREAM TEAM!

FIND THE ANSWERS FOR ALL THE PUZZLES AT THE BACK OF THE BOOK.

A VERY STRANGE SEASON

In 2020, the whole world was shaken by a virus, including the world of football. Here's a look at how Covid-19 has impacted the game, the players and the fans.

The Final Whistle

As the Covid virus spread around the world, football games were stopped to protect the players and spectators. The disruption to so many games resulted in new start and end dates for the football season.

UEFA CHAMPIONS LEAGUE®

Football Flashbacks

For a while, all we could watch were old replays. We did miss the excitement of new matches being played live, but it was also fun to look back at golden games from previous years.

Eventually restrictions were eased a little and football clubs were able to form bubbles. This helped to protect players, managers and support staff, and allowed matches to finally start being played again.

Silent Stadiums

For most games, no fans are allowed in the stadiums. There are no crowds to cheer their teams on and instead, people watching games on their devices can choose whether or not to have the sounds of shouting and clapping played in the background.

Showing Covid A Red Card

Football has found a way to continue and fans are, once again, able to enjoy the beautiful game. New rules and restrictions mean lots has changed but matches are being played in the stadiums and are back on our screens.

TOP SCORERS GIANT GRID

Look at this list of top goal scorers from Europe's top teams, then see if you can spot them in the grid opposite.

- ☐ **ROBERT LEWANDOWSKI**
- ☐ **CRISTIANO RONALDO**
- ☐ **MARCUS RASHFORD**
- ☐ **RAHEEM STERLING**
- ☐ **KARIM BENZEMA**
- ☐ **ROMELU LUKAKU**
- ☐ **LIONEL MESSI**
- ☐ **EDEN HAZARD**
- ☐ **SADIO MANÉ**
- ☐ **OLIVIER GIROUD**
- ☐ **ERLING HAALAND**

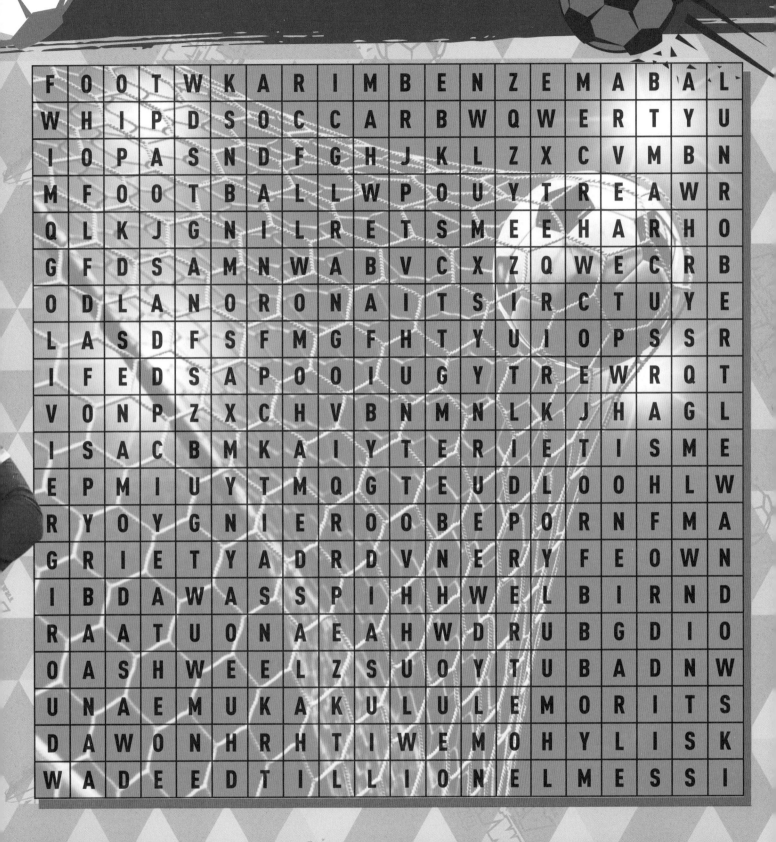

F	O	O	T	W	K	A	R	I	M	B	E	N	Z	E	M	A	B	A	L
W	H	I	P	D	S	O	C	C	A	R	B	W	Q	W	E	R	T	Y	U
I	O	P	A	S	N	D	F	G	H	J	K	L	Z	X	C	V	M	B	N
M	F	O	O	T	B	A	L	L	W	P	O	U	Y	T	R	E	A	W	R
Q	L	K	J	G	N	I	L	R	E	T	S	M	E	E	H	A	R	H	O
G	F	D	S	A	M	N	W	A	B	V	C	X	Z	Q	W	E	C	R	B
O	D	L	A	N	O	R	O	N	A	I	T	S	I	R	C	T	U	Y	E
L	A	S	D	F	S	F	M	G	F	H	T	Y	U	I	O	P	S	S	R
I	F	E	D	S	A	P	O	O	I	U	G	Y	T	R	E	W	R	Q	T
V	O	N	P	Z	X	C	H	V	B	N	M	L	K	J	H	A	G	L	
I	S	A	C	B	M	K	A	I	Y	T	E	R	I	E	T	I	S	M	E
E	P	M	I	U	Y	T	M	Q	G	T	E	U	D	L	O	O	H	L	W
R	Y	O	Y	G	N	I	E	R	O	O	B	E	P	O	R	N	F	M	A
G	R	I	E	T	Y	A	D	R	D	V	N	E	R	Y	F	E	O	W	N
I	B	D	A	W	A	S	S	P	I	H	H	W	E	L	B	I	R	N	D
R	A	A	T	U	O	N	A	E	A	H	W	D	R	U	B	G	D	I	O
O	A	S	H	W	E	E	L	Z	S	U	O	Y	T	U	B	A	D	N	W
U	N	A	E	M	U	K	A	K	U	L	U	L	E	M	O	R	I	T	S
D	A	W	O	N	H	R	H	T	I	W	E	M	O	H	Y	L	I	S	K
W	A	D	E	E	D	T	I	L	L	I	O	N	E	L	M	E	S	S	I

GOOOOOOAL!

CREATE A KIT

Which team do you support? Design a new home kit and an away kit for them. Go wild with the patterns and colours so the players will really stand out on the pitch!

MY TEAM:

AWAY

WHERE IN THE WORLD?

Check out the questions on the page, grab a pen and mark the answers on the map.

GREENLAND

ICELAND

CANADA

UNITED STATES

MEXICO

CUBA

SAN SALVADOR

PANAMA

VENEZUELA

COLOMBIA

EQUADOR

PERU

BRAZIL

BOLIVIA

CHILE

PARAGUAY

URUGUAY

ARGENTINA

UNITED KINGDOM

IRELAND

FRANCE

PORTUGAL

SPAIN

MOROCCO

ALGERIA

WESTERN SAHARA

MAURITANIA

MALI

SENEGAL

CAPE VERDE

GAMBIA

GUINEA BISSAU

GUINEA

SIERRA LEONE

LIBERIA

COTE D'IVORE

BURKINA FASO

BENIN

TOGO

GHANA

Samuel Eto'o has been on the UEFA Champions League winning team three times. Which continent is he from?

Where was Lionel Messi born?

Rakuten

10

12

Where does Juventus F.C. play?

JUVENTUS

Where do teams compete in the Bundesliga?

SWEDEN

FINLAND

ESTONIA

LATVIA

LITHUANIA

BELARUS

POLAND

UKRAINE

HUNGARY

ROMANIA

CROATIA

SERBIA

BULGARIA

GREECE

TURKEY

SYRIA

IRAQ

IRAN

LIBYA

EGYPT

SAUDI ARABIA

OMAN

CHAD

SUDAN

ERITREA

DJIBOUTI

YEMEN

CENTRAL AFRICAN REP.

ETHIOPIA

SOMALIA

CONGO

D.R. OF THE CONGO

UGANDA

KENYA

TANZANIA

ANGOLA

ZAMBIA

MALAWI

NAMIBIA

ZIMBABWE

MOZAMBIQUE

MADAGASCAR

BOTSWANA

SWAZILAND

SAUTH AFRICA

RUSSIA

KAZAKHSTAN

MONGOLIA

UZBEKISTAN

KYRGYSTAN

TURKMENISTAN

AFGANISTAN

PAKISTAN

NEPAL

CHINA

INDIA

BURMA

THAILAND

VIETNAM

PHILIPPINES

MALAYSIA

INDONESIA

NORTH COREA

SOUTH COREA

JAPAN

PAPUA NEW GUINEA

AUSTRALIA

SYDNEY

CANBERRA

NEW ZELAND

NEW ZELEND

Where was the game of football, as we know it today, invented?

The 2020/21 UEFA Champions League final was played at the Atatürk Olympic Stadium, which is where?

ON A RUN

Find the right path and take this player the whole length of the pitch to score a goal. Watch out for the opposition players, waiting to tackle and take the ball!

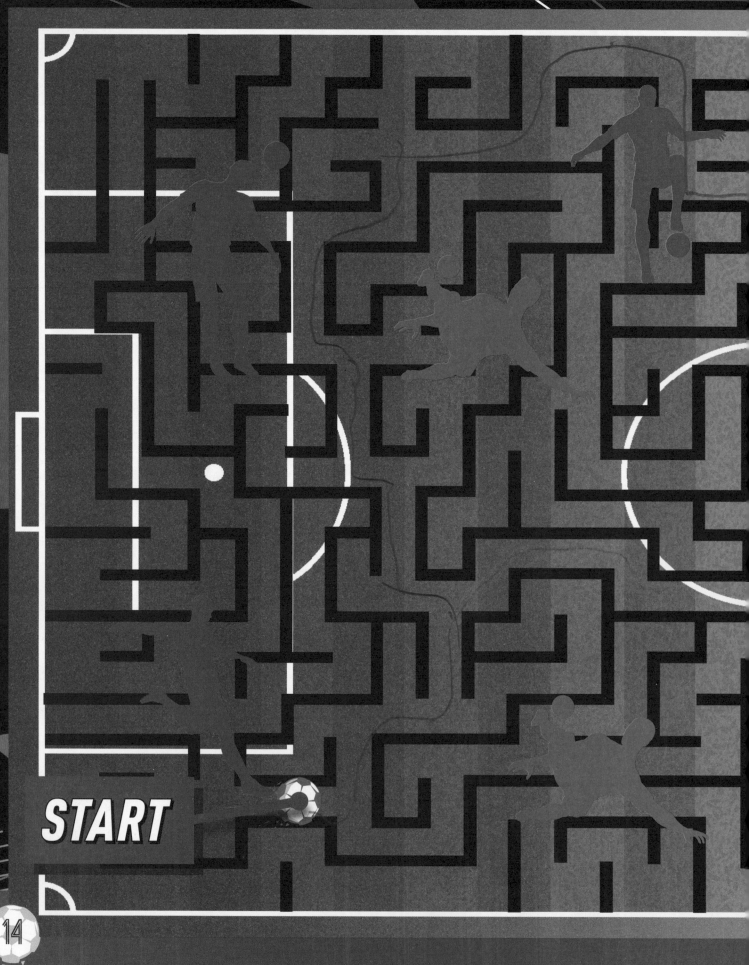

START

GOOOOOOAL!

END

15

MANCHESTER UNITED

PROFILE

Full name:
MANCHESTER UNITED FOOTBALL CLUB

Founded:
1878

Coach:
OLE GUNNAR SOLSKJÆR

Captain:
HARRY MAGUIRE

Ground:
OLD TRAFFORD

No. of UEFA Champions League wins:
3

UEFA ranking:
8

Group H:
LOSERS (W3 D0 L3)

European Cup best:
**WINNERS
1968, 1999, 2008**

DREAM TEAM

MANCHESTER CITY

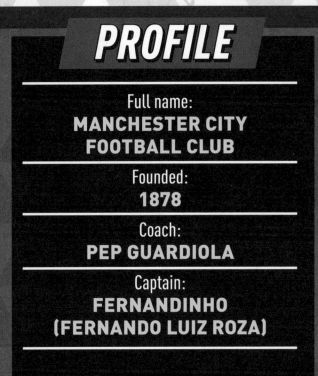

PROFILE

Full name:
MANCHESTER CITY FOOTBALL CLUB

Founded:
1878

Coach:
PEP GUARDIOLA

Captain:
FERNANDINHO (FERNANDO LUIZ ROZA)

Ground:
CITY OF MANCHESTER STADIUM (ETIHAD STADIUM)

No. of UEFA Champions League wins:
0

UEFA ranking:
6

Group C:
WINNERS (W5 D1 L0)

European Cup best:
SEMI-FINALS 2016

COUNTING KIT

The match is over and it's time to wash the team kit. Can you count up how many of each item you have to wash? Fill in the answers below.

SHIRTS: ....

SHORTS: ....

SOCKS: ....

18

MATCH DAY MIX-UP

Uh oh, the football commentators have got their words in a jumble!
Unscramble the letters to reveal the football terms they're talking about.

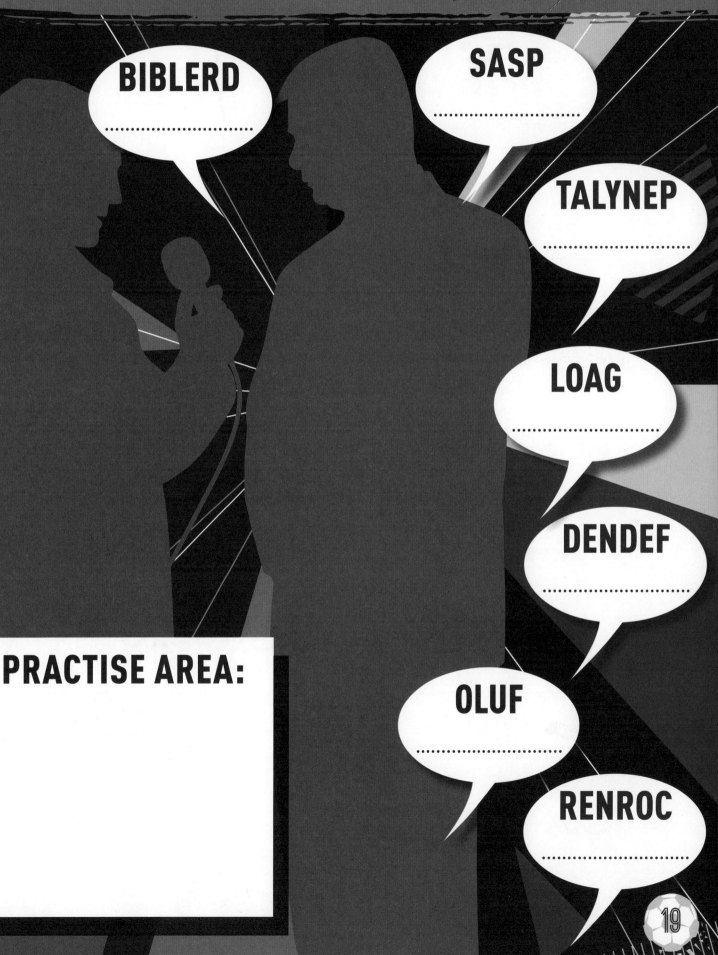

BIBLERD
....

SASP
....

TALYNEP
....

LOAG
....

DENDEF
....

PRACTISE AREA:

OLUF
....

RENROC
....

FANTASTIC FOOTBALL FACTS

Whether you're a player or a fan of the beautiful game, or both, here's a little history and interesting info about your fave sport.

An early version of football was played in China over 2000 years ago. Way back then, the game was called 'Cuju'.

Around 250 million people play football in over 200 countries, making it the world's most popular sport.

Apparently the first man to walk on the moon, astronaut Neil Armstrong, wanted to take a football into space, but NASA refused his request. What a shame – imagine how cool a game of space soccer would have been!

The highest number of goals ever scored in a single football game is 149! They were all own goals, scored by team Stade Olympique de l'Emyrne. They gave away the huge win to AS Adema as a protest against a referee decision in a previous game.

The highest transfer fee ever paid for a footballer was in 2017 for Neymar. He moved from Barcelona to Paris Saint-Germain for a staggering £198 million!

Star striker Zlatan Ibrahimovic has never won the UEFA Champions League, despite having played for seven clubs – Ajax, Barcelona, Inter Milan, Juventus, AC Milan, Paris Saint-Germain and Man United – that have won the trophy.

Unofficially, the number 10 shirt is worn by the best player in the team. Some famous footballers to have donned the prized jersey include Lionel Messi for Barcelona, Arjen Robben for Bayern Munich, Eden Hazard for Chelsea and Zlatan Ibrahimovic for PSG.

PENALTY SHOOT OUT

Hang out with your BFF and play a fun game of Penalty Shoot Out together.

Have a good look at the footballers on these pages, then cover each of them with a piece of paper. Take it in turns to pick up two pieces of paper, one from each page. If the footballers underneath match, keep the pieces of paper. If they don't match, put the pieces of paper back. When all of the footballers have been uncovered, the player with the most pieces of paper wins.

Decide who will be Player 1 and who will be Player 2.
Every time you make a match, you hit the back of the net and get to colour in a ball!

PLAYER 1

PLAYER 2

SOCCER SPINNER

Follow the simple steps below to create a soccer spinner so you can practise a different football skill every day.

HOW TO MAKE:

- Remove the page opposite and glue it to a thin piece of card.
- Cut around the dotted lines to cut out the spinner template.
- Fold in half and glue together, so the design is facing outwards.
- Push a pencil through the middle (where x marks the spot).

HOW TO PLAY:

Each day, twirl the pencil to spin the spinner. Whichever side rests on table when it stops is the skill you should practise that day!

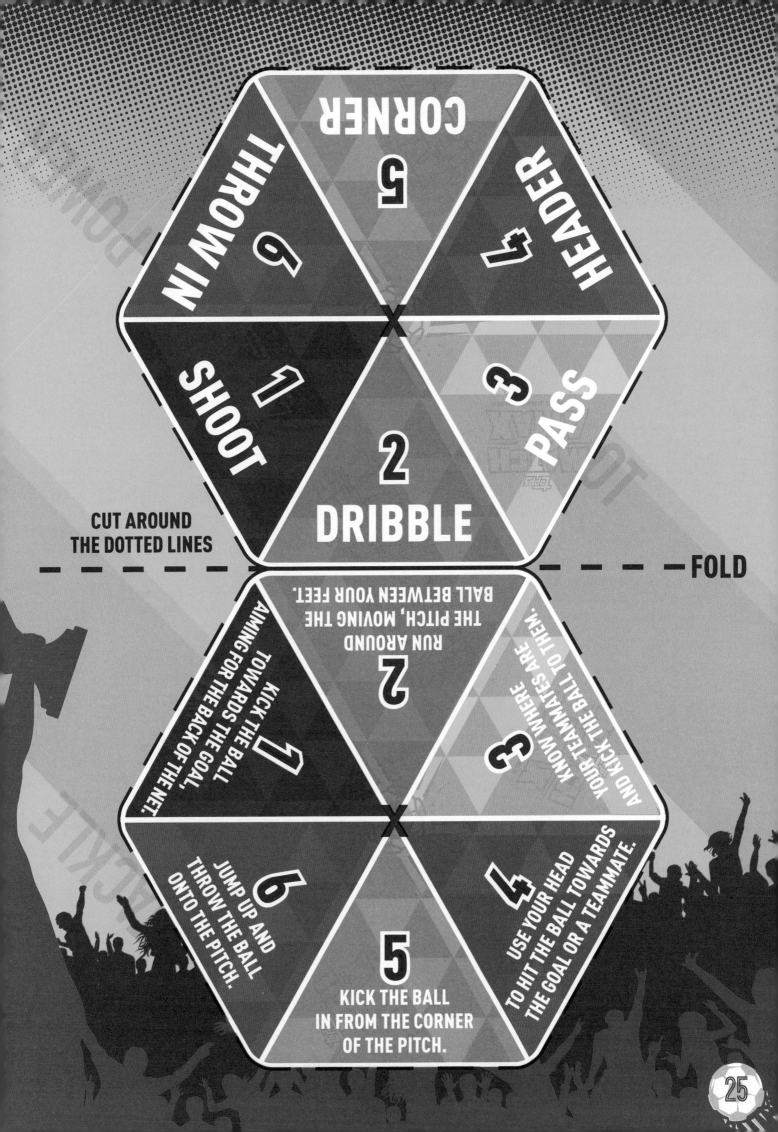

CUT AROUND
THE DOTTED LINES

— — — FOLD

CORNER 5

THROW IN 6

HEADER 4

SHOOT 1

PASS 3

DRIBBLE 2

1 KICK THE BALL TOWARDS THE GOAL, AIMING FOR THE BACK OF THE NET.

2 RUN AROUND THE PITCH, MOVING THE BALL BETWEEN YOUR FEET.

3 KNOW WHERE ARE YOUR TEAMMATES TO THEM. AND KICK THE BALL TO THEM.

4 USE YOUR HEAD TO HIT THE BALL TOWARDS THE GOAL OR A TEAMMATE.

5 KICK THE BALL IN FROM THE CORNER OF THE PITCH.

6 JUMP UP AND THROW THE BALL ONTO THE PITCH.

SOCCER SPINNER BACK

GLUE HERE

FOLD — — — — — — —

GLUE HERE

BOOTS AND BALLS!

Grab a pal and play a couple of games of Boots And Balls.

HOW TO PLAY:

1. Pick which player is Boots and which is Balls.
2. Take turns to draw your picture of a boot or a ball.
3. The first player to get three in a row – straight across, down or diagonally – wins!

GAME 1

GAME 2

27

BARCELONA

PROFILE

Full name:
**FUTBOL CLUB
BARCELONA**

Founded:
1899

Coach:
RONALD KOEMAN

Captain:
LIONEL MESSI

Ground:
CAMP NOU

No. of UEFA Champions League wins:
5

UEFA ranking:
2

Group G:
RUNNERS-UP (W5 D0 L1)

European Cup best:
**WINNERS
1992, 2006, 2009, 2011, 2015**

REAL MADRID

PROFILE

Full name:
REAL MADRID CLUB DE FÚTBOL

Founded:
1902

Coach:
ZINÉDINE ZIDANE

Captain:
SERGIO RAMOS

Ground:
SANTIAGO BERNABÉU STADIUM

No. of UEFA Champions League wins:
13

UEFA ranking:
3

Group B:
WINNERS (W3 D1 L2)

European Cup best:
WINNERS
1956, 1957, 1958, 1959, 1960, 1966, 1998, 2000, 2002, 2014, 2016, 2017, 2018)

TOP SCORER

These two players are competing to be named Top Scorer this season. Add the numbers right up to the top to see which of them scored the most goals.

PLAYER 1

3		5
1	2	2	3

PLAYER 2

3	4	
2	1	3	1

FOOTBALLER DANCE-OFF

Practise these fantastic footballer moves and then prepare a match-day celebratory dance!

HOW TO PLAY:

TAKE TURNS ROLLING THE DICE AND WRITE DOWN THE NUMBERS YOU ROLL. ROLL 10 TIMES EACH.

EVERY NUMBER ON THE DICE MATCHES A FOOTBALL MOVE. WRITE DOWN THE 10 FOOTBALL MOVES YOU ROLLED.

WATCH THE MATCH AND WHENEVER YOUR TEAM SCORES, PUT ALL THE MOVES YOU ROLLED TOGETHER AND PERFORM A CELEBRATORY DANCE LIKE THE STAR PLAYER YOU ARE!

YOU WILL NEED:

1 DICE

A DANCE PARTNER (OPTIONAL)

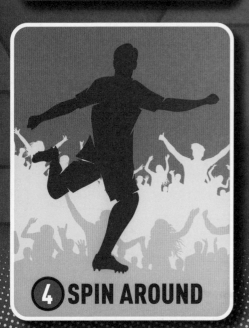

1 STRETCH UP

2 SLIDE IN

3 CROUCH DOWN

4 SPIN AROUND

5 JUMP UP

6 KICK IT

YOUR PLAYER PROFILE

Create your own footballer profile by filling in the details below.

Name:

Team you play for:

Coach:

Position:

Shirt number:

No. of goals scored last season:

Best in-game moment:

Team you support:

Footballing hero:

STICK OR DRAW
YOUR PICTURE HERE.

GUESS WHO?

Can you work out which coaches are being described from this list, in the descriptions below?

Ronald Koeman
Zinédine Zidane
André Villas-Boas
Mauricio Pochettino
Ole Gunnar Solskjær
Hans-Dieter Flick
Edin Terzić
Pep Guardiola
Andrea Pirlo
Antonio Conte

COACH 1

This Norwegian coach once played for the Red Devils. He scored a last-minute goal for them in injury time to win the 1999 UEFA Champions League Final.

COACH:

COACH 2

This Spanish coach once player for, and then captained, Barcelona. In 2008 he became their coach and in his first season, the team won UEFA Champions League.

COACH:

COACH 3

This French coach once played for Real Madrid. He scored one of the greatest UEFA Champions League goals ever, winning the 2002 Final for Real with a left-footed volley.

COACH:

Now try to work out which players are being described from this list, in the descriptions below.

Fernandinho
Lionel Messi
Sergio Ramos
Steve Mandanda
Marquinhos
Manuel Neuer
Marco Reus
Giorgio Chiellini
Harry Maguire
Samir Handanovič

PLAYER 1

This Argentinian player has won four UEFA Champions League titles with the team he has played with for his whole footballing career.

PLAYER:

PLAYER 2

This Spanish player has won four UEFA Champions League titles with his current team, who he has played for since 2005.

PLAYER:

PLAYER 3

This English player has not yet won a UEFA Champions League title, with either his previous or current team.

PLAYER:

IT'S DERBY DAY!

Can you match up the local rivalries between these UEFA Champions League teams?

Barcelona

Manchester United

Bayern Munich

Marseille

Borussia Dortmund

Inter Milan

Juventus

Real Madrid

Manchester City

Paris Saint-Germain

A NUMBERS GAME

Set a stopwatch and see how long it takes you to work out these football figures, facts and stats.

1

How many players are in a football team?

ANSWER:

2

Not including stoppages, how many minutes are in a football match?

ANSWER:

3

What number shirt does the goalkeeper traditionally wear?

ANSWER:

4

How many teams qualified for the UEFA Champions League group stage in 2020/21?

ANSWER:

5

How many players were allowed on the match sheet in 2020/21?

ANSWER:

6

What is the capacity at Istanbul's Atatürk Olympic Stadium?

ANSWER:

7

Cristiano Ronaldo is the top UEFA Champions League scorer. How many goals has he scored, excluding qualifying?

ANSWER:

8

In total, how many players have scored hat-tricks in the UEFA Champions League?

ANSWER:

MARSEILLE

PROFILE

Full name:
OLYMPIQUE DE MARSEILLE

Founded:
1899

Coach:
JORGE SAMPAOLI

Captain:
STEVE MANDANDA

Ground:
STADE VÉLODROME

No. of UEFA Champions League wins:
1

UEFA ranking:
57

Group C:
LOSERS (W1 D0 L5)

European Cup best:
**WINNERS
1993**

DREAM TEAM

PARIS SAINT-GERMAIN

PROFILE

Full name:
PARIS SAINT-GERMAIN FOOTBALL CLUB

Founded:
1970

Coach:
MAURICIO POCHETTINO

Captain:
MARQUINHOS (MARCOS AOÁS CORRÊA)

Ground:
PARC DES PRINCES

No. of UEFA Champions League wins:
0

UEFA ranking:
7

Group B:
WINNERS (W4 D0 L2)

European Cup best:
FINAL 2020

HE SHOOTS, HE SCORES!

This player is practising his shooting. Which ball will not go in goal?

It's the only one with an odd number on....

THE BEST BADGES

Look closely to identity the badges and then write the team names in the correct spaces.

41

SOCCER CARDS

Create some Match Attax player cards for your footballing teammates, giving their attacking and defending skills a score out of 10. Pick 11 main players and also select 7 super subs. When you're done, cut out the cards and use them to play a game with your friends and family.

FORWARDS

Forwards must be super-fast on their feet and have a spot-on aim, so be sure to select them wisely.

GOALKEEPER

Who will you choose to wear the all-important number 1 shirt? They must have quick reactions and good hands.

If you don't play for a team then here's a chance to create your own! Select players from your friends and schoolmates.

MIDFIELDERS

Your choices for midfield should stay alert at all times and be ready run forwards or drop back as needed.

DEFENDERS

Pick defenders who will keep calm and stay strong whenever the opposition players go on the attack.

PIC OF PLAYER

Name:
Position:
Shirt number:
Attacking skills: /100
Defending skills: /100

PIC OF PLAYER

Name:
Position:
Shirt number:
Attacking skills: /100
Defending skills: /100

PIC OF PLAYER

Name:
Position:
Shirt number:
Attacking skills: /100
Defending skills: /100

PIC OF PLAYER

Name:
Position:
Shirt number:
Attacking skills: /100
Defending skills: /100

PIC OF PLAYER

Name:
Position:
Shirt number:
Attacking skills: /100
Defending skills: /100

PIC OF PLAYER

Name:
Position:
Shirt number:
Attacking skills: /100
Defending skills: /100

PIC OF PLAYER

Name:
Position:
Shirt number:
Attacking skills: /100
Defending skills: /100

PIC OF PLAYER

Name:
Position:
Shirt number:
Attacking skills: /100
Defending skills: /100

PIC OF PLAYER

Name:
Position:
Shirt number:
Attacking skills: /100
Defending skills: /100

PIC OF PLAYER

Name:
Position:
Shirt number:
Attacking skills: /100
Defending skills: /100

PIC OF PLAYER

Name:
Position:
Shirt number:
Attacking skills: /100
Defending skills: /100

PIC OF PLAYER

Name:
Position:
Shirt number:
Attacking skills: /100
Defending skills: /100

PIC OF PLAYER

Name:
Position:
Shirt number:
Attacking skills: /100
Defending skills: /100

PIC OF PLAYER

Name:
Position:
Shirt number:
Attacking skills: /100
Defending skills: /100

PIC OF PLAYER

Name:
Position:
Shirt number:
Attacking skills: /100
Defending skills: /100

PIC OF PLAYER

Name:
Position:
Shirt number:
Attacking skills: /100
Defending skills: /100

PIC OF PLAYER

Name:
Position:
Shirt number:
Attacking skills: /100
Defending skills: /100

PIC OF PLAYER

Name:
Position:
Shirt number:
Attacking skills: /100
Defending skills: /100

BEFORE THE WHISTLE BLOWS

How many words can you make out of the letters in UEFA Champions League in two minutes? Set your stopwatch... GO!

UEFA CHAMPIONS LEAGUE

TEN TRICKY CHALLENGES

Sharpen your football skills by attempting these challenges. Your teammates will be impressed!

CHALLENGE 1:
Line up a row of cones (or sofa cushions) and then see how quickly you can dribble the ball between them. Then try it there and back again.

CHALLENGE 2:
Can you do 10 keepy-uppys using your feet?

CHALLENGE 3:
Can you do 10 keepy-uppys using your knee?

CHALLENGE 4:
Line up several balls in a row in front of a goal and then, without pausing, see how many you can score.

CHALLENGE 5:
How long can you balance the ball on your head?

CHALLENGE 6:
How long can you balance the ball between your shoulder blades?

CHALLENGE 7:
Practise your aim by placing a target and then keep on kicking until you can hit it every time.

CHALLENGE 8:
Try doing toe taps on the ball for as long as possible – how long can you keep going for and how many can you do?

CHALLENGE 9:
Now do some side foot taps – again, how long can you keep going for and how many can you do?

CHALLENGE 10:
Practise your passing and receiving skills by kicking the ball against a wall so it bounces back to you.

BAYERN MUNICH

PROFILE

Full name:
FUSSBALL-CLUB BAYERN MÜNCHEN E. V.

Founded:
1900

Coach:
HANS-DIETER FLICK

Captain:
MANUEL NEUER

Ground:
ALLIANZ ARENA

No. of UEFA Champions League wins:
6

UEFA ranking:
1

Group A:
WINNERS (W5 D1 L0)

European Cup best:
WINNERS
1974, 1975, 1976, 2001, 2013, 2020

Bayern Munich are the **current champs** – they **won the UEFA Champions League** last season!

BORUSSIA DORTMUND

PROFILE

Full name:
BALLSPIELVEREIN BORUSSIA 09 E.V. DORTMUND

Founded:
1909

Coach:
EDIN TERZIĆ

Captain:
MARCO REUS

Ground:
WESTFALENSTADION

No. of UEFA Champions League wins:
1

UEFA ranking:
13

Group F:
WINNERS
W4 D1 L1

European Cup best:
WINNERS
1997

PLAYER PAIRS

The team is warming up before the match. Draw lines to link each pair of player poses.

SING FOR A WIN!

Write a catchy chant for your team, for their fans to shout or sing whenever they score.

If you need a little inspiration...

FOREVER
HEART
GREATEST

WINNERS
SHOOT
CHAMPIONS
HOME

GET TO THE GOAL

Follow the directions to plot the red player's path around the football pitch avoiding the blue players to help him score a goal.

DIRECTIONS:

RUN NORTH FOR THREE SQUARES

SLIDE EAST FOR FIVE SQUARES

JOG NORTH FOR FOUR SQUARES

DRIBBLE WEST FOR FOUR SQUARES

RACE SOUTH FOR TWO SQUARES

DASH WEST FOR FOUR SQUARES

SPRINT NORTH FOR FIVE SQUARES

DRIBBLE EAST FOR SIX SQUARES

TURN NORTH, RUN FIVE SQUARES AND SHOOT!

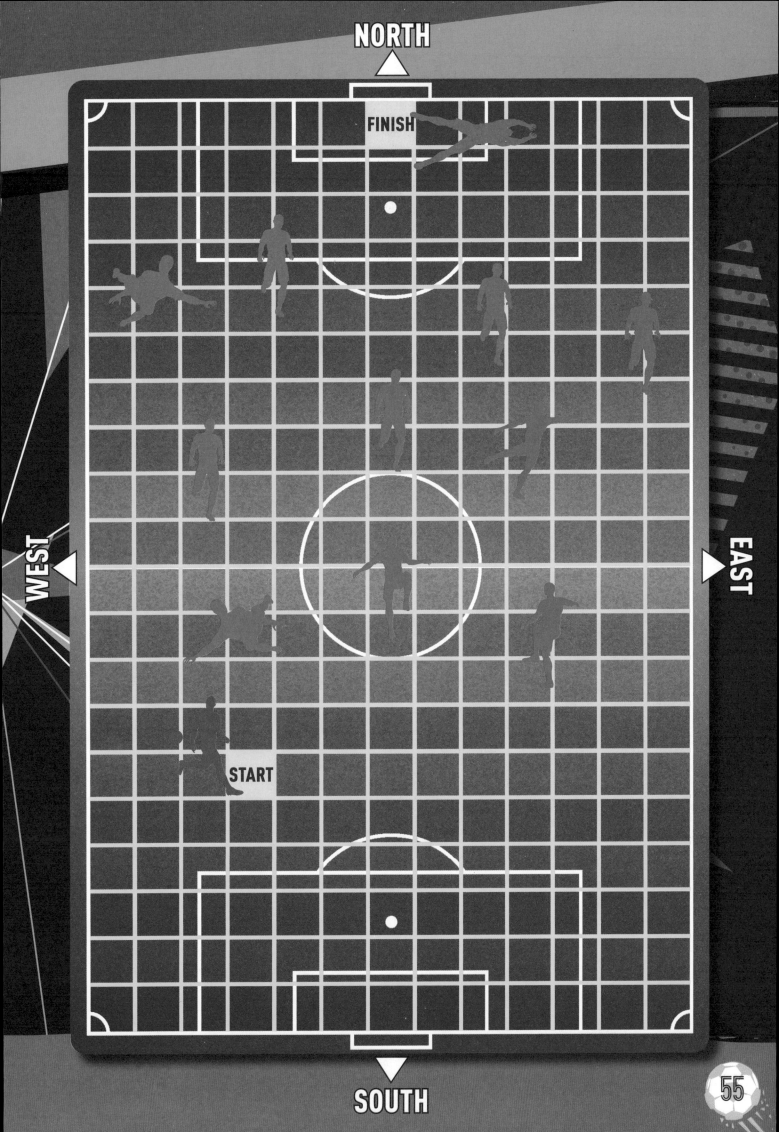

FINISH

WEST

EAST

START

FINISH

ODD BALL OUT

Can you spot and circle the football that is different to the others in each pile?

A CUP FOR CHAMPIONS

Sadly, these days the UEFA Champions League winners don't get to keep the real trophy. Design a new take-home trophy, fit for football royalty!

THE CURRENT UEFA CHAMPIONS LEAGUE TROPHY WAS DESIGNED BY JÜRG STADELMANN AND TOOK 340 HOURS TO MAKE. IT IS 73.5cm TALL AND WEIGHS 7.5kg.

FOOTBALL FUNNIES

Score some laughs with these ha-ha-larious jokes about the beautiful game.

Ha Ha!

How do football players stay cool?

ANSWER: They stand close to the fans.

Tee-Hee!

What is a ghost's favourite football position?

ANSWER: Ghoulkeeper

Ha Ha!

What did the referee say to the chicken that tripped up a player?

ANSWER: Fowl!

Tee-Hee!

What does Cristiano Ronaldo have in common with a magician?

ANSWER: They both perform hat-tricks!

Ha Ha!

Why don't grasshoppers watch football?

ANSWER: They prefer cricket.

58

Ha Ha!

Why was the best footballer in the world asked to tidy his room?

ANSWER: Because he was Messi.

Tee-Hee!

What happened when the pitch flooded?

ANSWER: The teams used their subs.

Ha Ha!

It's not raining, so how did the football pitch get wet?

ANSWER: The players dribbled all over it.

Tee-Hee!

How do you upset a footballer on their birthday?

ANSWER: Give them a Red Card.

Tee-Hee!

Which team in the 2020/21 UEFA Champions League have the chilliest ground?

ANSWER: Cold Trafford.

DREAM TEAM

JUVENTUS

PROFILE

Full name:
JUVENTUS
FOOTBALL CLUB

Founded:
1897

Coach:
ANDREA PIRLO

Captain:
GIORGIO CHIELLINI

Ground:
JUVENTUS STADIUM

No. of UEFA Champions League wins:
2

UEFA ranking:
4

Group G:
WINNERS (W5 D0 L1)

European Cup best:
WINNERS
1985, 1996

INTER MILAN

PROFILE

Full name:
FOOTBALL CLUB INTERNAZIONALE MILANO

Founded:
1908

Coach:
ANTONIO CONTE

Captain:
SAMIR HANDANOVIČ

Ground:
SAN SIRO

No. of UEFA Champions League wins:
3

UEFA ranking:
25

Group B:
LOSERS (W1 D3 L2)

European Cup best:
**WINNERS
1964, 1965, 2010**

FEELIN' LUCKY

Can you find the pair of lucky goalkeeper gloves?
They're the only matching pair that appear once on the page.

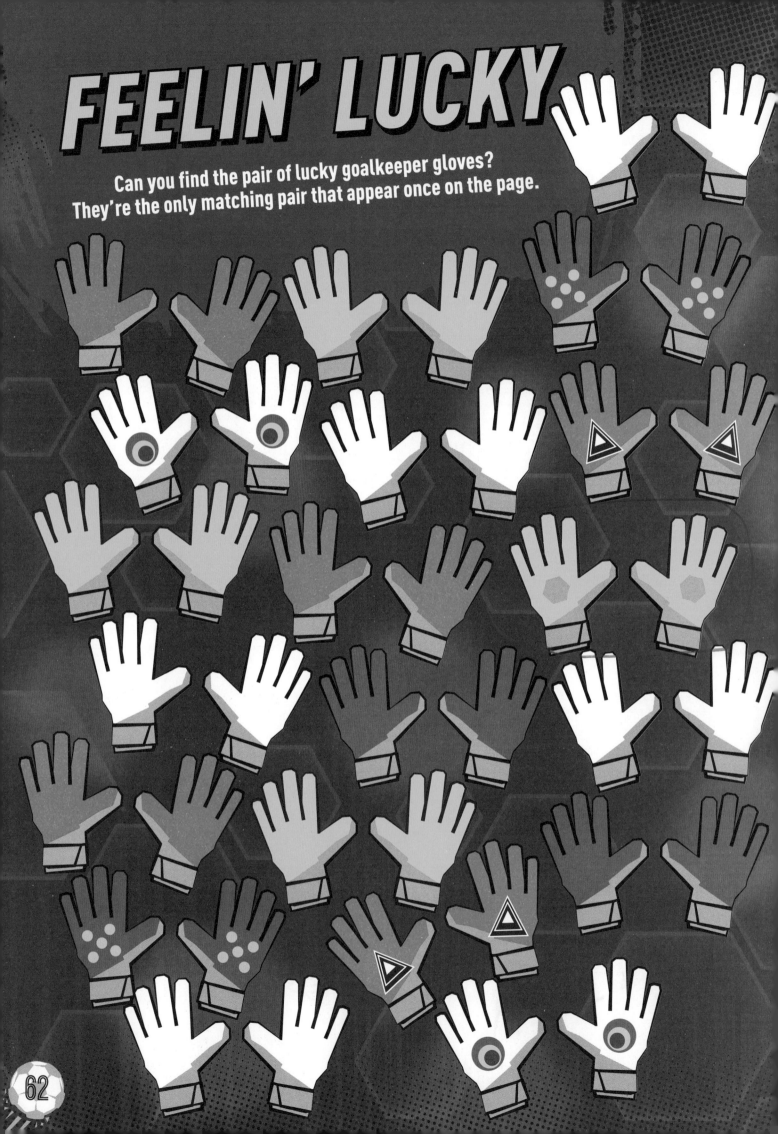

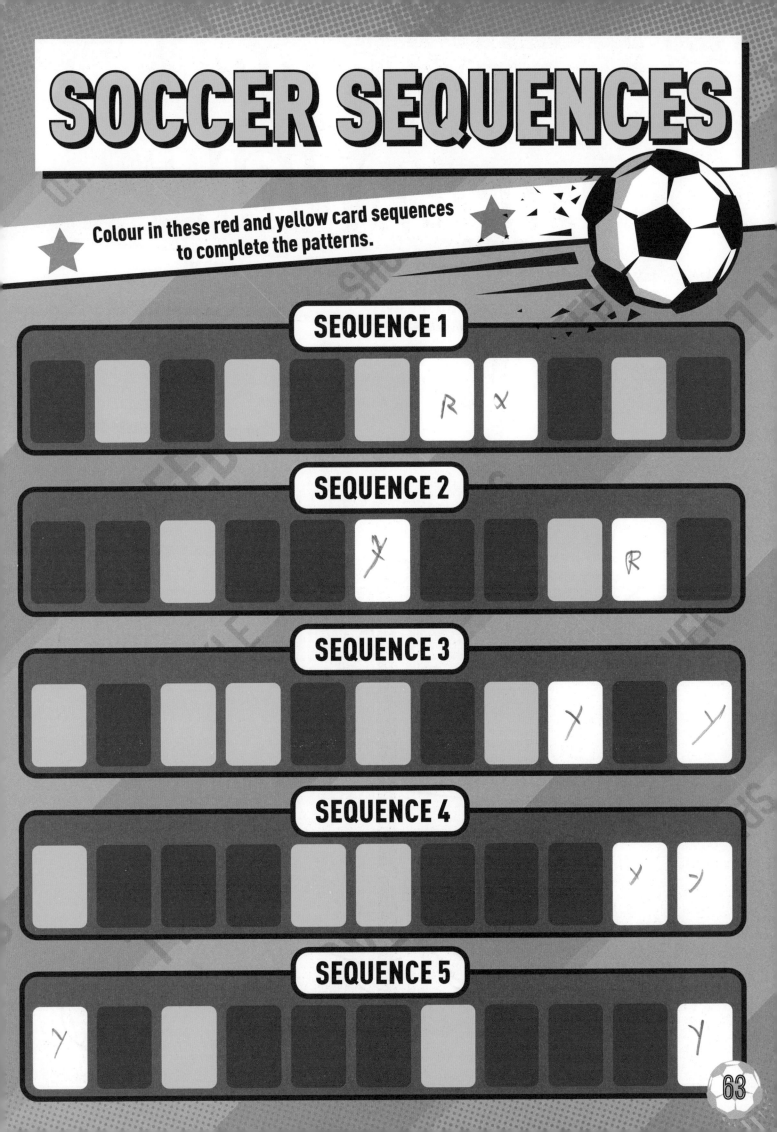

SOCCER SEQUENCES

Colour in these red and yellow card sequences to complete the patterns.

SEQUENCE 1

SEQUENCE 2

SEQUENCE 3

SEQUENCE 4

SEQUENCE 5

63

AMAZING FORMATIONS

Can you match the pictures of these popular football formations with the corresponding numbers?

★★★ ★★★

4-4-2 ³

4-5-1 ⁶

4-3-3 ²

4-2-3-1 ¹

3-4-3 ⁵

4-1-4-1 ⁴

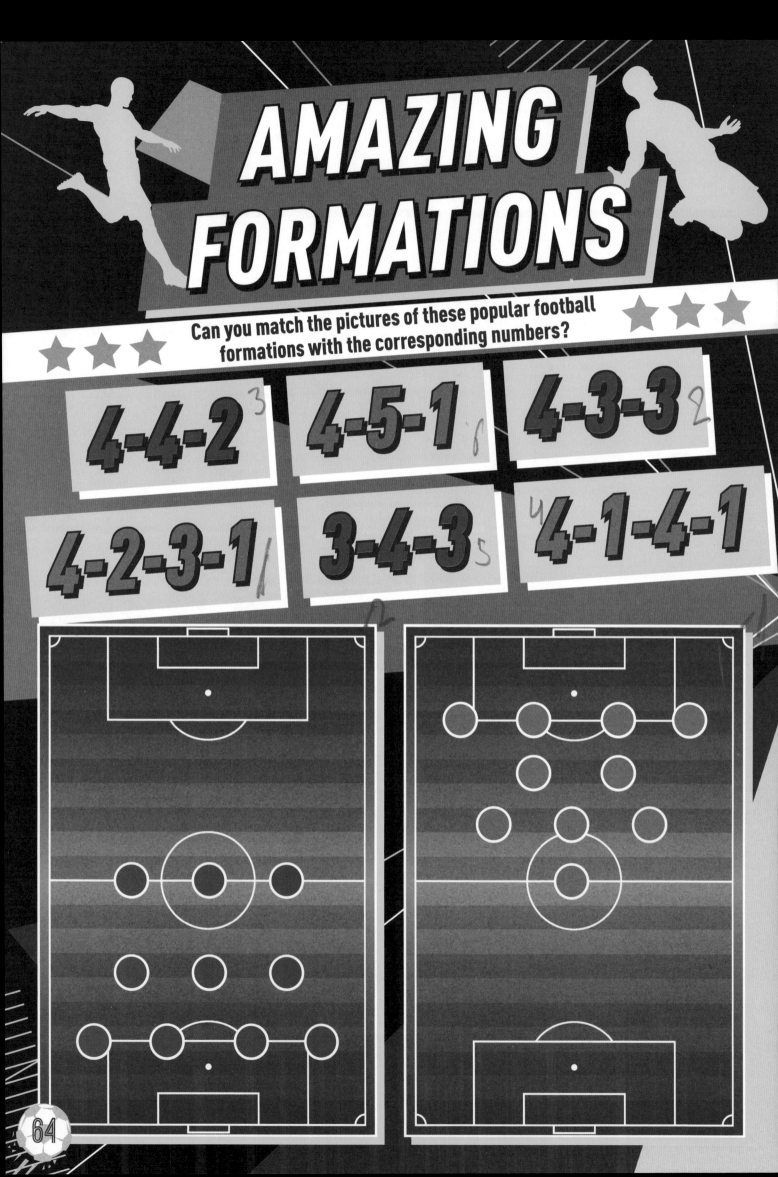

64

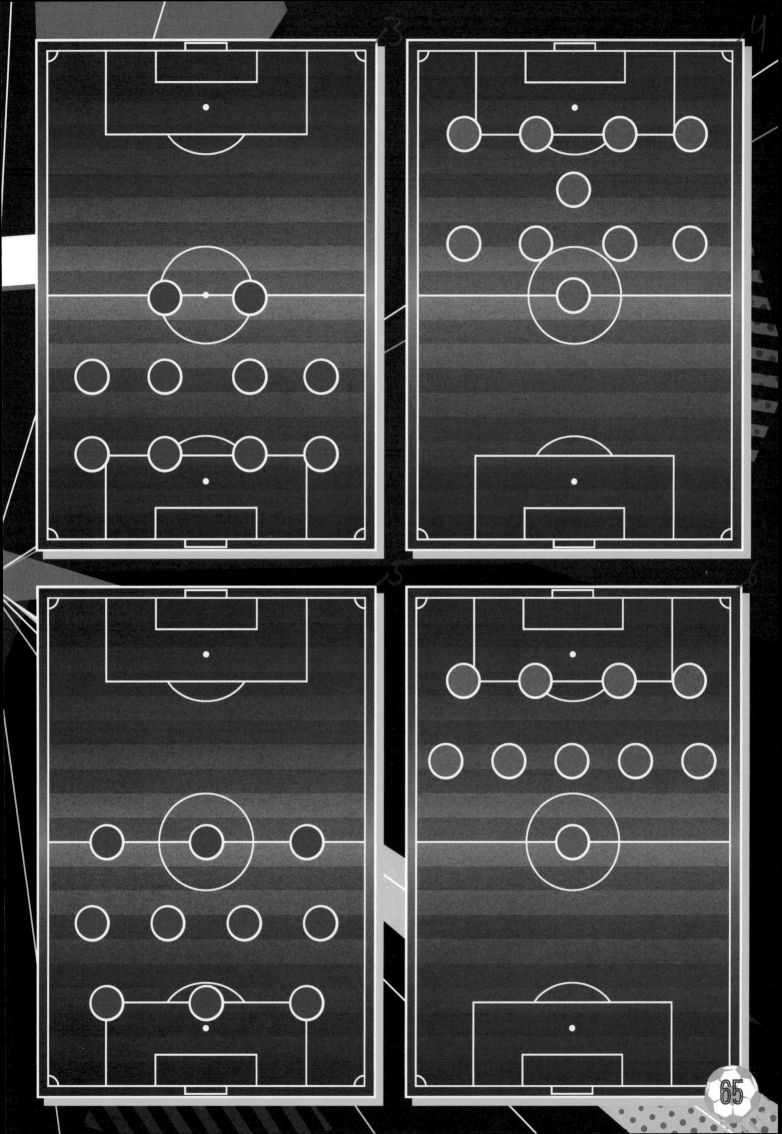

BLINGIN' BOOTS

Some footballers like to wear their personality on their boots!
Design a pair of boots that show off your personality.

RESULT MEMORY

Can you remember the final scores of these five historic UEFA Champions League finals?

YEAR	TEAMS	RESULT	MATCH ANALYSIS
1997	Borussia Dortmund vs Juventus	__ - __	The reigning champions couldn't keep hold of the cup....
1999	Manchester United vs Bayern Munich	__ - __	Perhaps most famous three minutes of stoppage time in football history.
2013	Borussia Dortmund vs Bayern Munich	__ - __	The winning goal was scored in the 89th minute.
2014	Real Madrid vs Atlético Madrid	__ - __	The winning team scored three goals in just 10 minutes.
2015	Juventus vs Barcelona	__ - __	Both teams were trying for a Treble after winning domestic league and cup competitions....

WIN, LOSE OR DRAW

Here's a fun, football-focused game for two teams of friends to play.

HOW TO PLAY:

Form two teams, with the same number of people in each. Write the words from the list below on separate pieces of paper, fold them in half and put them in a bowl or hat. Each team should take it in turns to pick a piece of paper – just one team member should look at the paper and then draw what's on it. If the people in their team correctly guess the word within two minutes, they win a point. If they can't, the other team gets one guess to win the point. The winners are the team with the most points when all of the pieces of paper have been picked.

WORDS TO DRAW/GUESS:

CAPTAIN

HALF TIME

HEADER

CORNER

DRIBBLE

RED FLAG

CROSSBAR

GOLDEN BOOT

COACH

FOUL

CELEBRATION SNAP

Add the missing pieces to complete this photo of the team celebrating a victory.

69

UEFA
CHAMPIONS LEAGUE QUIZ

Are you ready to test your knowledge of the world's best club football tournament?

Q1.
What does UEFA stand for?

_____

_____

Q2.
When was the competition introduced, to replace the European Champion Clubs' Cup?

_____

_____

Q3.
The chorus of the UEFA Champions League anthem contains which three languages?

_____

_____

Q4.
Which team are the most successful in UEFA Champions League history so far?

_____

_____

Q5.
On what date did the 2019/20 UEFA Champions League end?

_____

Q6.

Which team won the 2019/20 UEFA Champions League?

_____

_____

Q7.

In what year did the Istanbul's Atatürk Olympic Stadium previously stage the UEFA Champions League final?

_____

Q8.

With 134 goals, excluding qualifying, who is the top UEFA Champions League scorer?

_____

Q9.

When club wins are combined, which three countries have had the highest number of UEFA Champions League victories?

_____

_____

_____

Q10.

Roy Makaay scored the fastest UEFA Champions League goal in just 10.2 seconds after kick-off against Real Madrid in 2007. What team did he play for?

_____

YOUR SCORE:

[   ] / 10

YOUR
DREAM TEAM

NAME
1
POSITION

NAME
2
POSITION

NAME
3
POSITION

NAME
4
POSITION

NAME
5
POSITION

NAME
6
POSITION

NAME
7
POSITION

NAME
8
POSITION

IT'S TIME TO PUT ALL RIVALRIES ASIDE AND PICK YOUR TOP 11 PLAYERS FROM THE TEAMS THAT TOOK PART IN THE 2020/21 UEFA CHAMPIONS LEAGUE.

NAME
9
POSITION

NAME
10
POSITION

NAME
11
POSITION

YOU GET TO SELECT 5 SUBSTITUTES, TOO!

Sub 1: _____
_____

Sub 2: _____
_____

Sub 3: _____
_____

Sub 4: _____
_____

Sub 5: _____
_____

Coach: _____
_____

ANSWERS

P8-9 TOP SCORERS GIANT GRID

```
F O O T W K A R I M B E N Z E M A B A L
W H I P D S O C C A R B W Q W E R T Y U
I O P A S N D F G H J K L Z X C V M B N
M F O O T B A L L W P O U Y T R E A W R
Q L K J G N I L R E T S M E E H A R H
G F D S A M N W A B V C X Z Q W E C R B
O D L A N O R O N A I T S I R C T U Y E
L A S D F S F M G F H T Y U I O P S S R
I F E D S A P O O I U G Y T R E W R Q T
V O N P Z X C H V B N M N L K J H A G L
I S A C B M K A I Y T E R I E T I S M E
E P M I U Y T M Q G T E U D L O O H L W
R Y O Y G N I E R O O B E P O R N F M A
G R I E T Y A D R D V N E R Y F E O W N
I B D A W A S S P I H H W E L B I R N D
R A A T U O N A E A H W D R U B G D I O
O A S H W E E L Z S U Q Y T U B A D N W
U N A E M U K A K U L U L E M O R I T S
D A W O N H R H T I W E M O H Y L I S K
W A D E E D T I L L I O N E L M E S S I
```

P12-13 WHERE IN THE WORLD?

⬡ = Argentina
⬡ = Africa
⬡ = Italy
⬡ = Germany
⬡ = England
⬡ = Istanbul

P14-15 ON A RUN

P18 COUNTING KIT

- Shirts = 9
- Shorts = 14
- Socks = 14

P19 MATCH DAY MIX-UP

- Dribble • Pass • Penalty • Goal • Defend
- Foul • Corner

P30 TOP SCORER

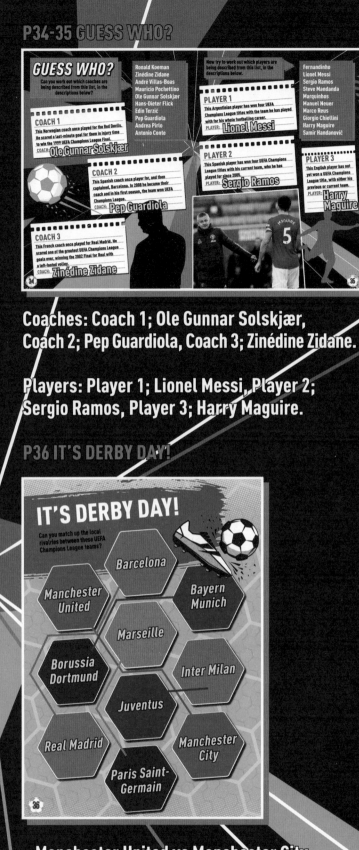

Coaches: Coach 1; Ole Gunnar Solskjær, Coach 2; Pep Guardiola, Coach 3; Zinédine Zidane.

Players: Player 1; Lionel Messi, Player 2; Sergio Ramos, Player 3; Harry Maguire.

P36 IT'S DERBY DAY!

- Manchester United vs Manchester City,
- Barcelona vs Real Madrid,
- Marseille vs Paris Saint-Germain,
- Bayern Munich vs Borussia Dortmund,
- Juventus vs Inter Milan.

P37 A NUMBERS GAME

Q1 – 11, Q2 – 90, Q3 – 1, Q4 – 32, Q5 – 23, including 5 substitutes, Q6 – 70,000, Q7 – 134, Q8 – 91

P40 HE SHOOTS, HE SCORES!

Ball 9

ANSWERS

P41 THE BEST BADGES

1. Marseille, 2. Barcelona, 3. Liverpool,
4. Rennes, 5. Sevilla, 6. Juventus, 7. Chelsea,
8. Lazio, 9. Atalanta

P54-55 GET TO THE GOAL

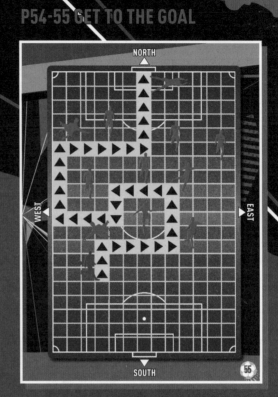

P56 ODD BALL OUT

P52 PLAYER PAIRS

78